What's Weird About A Mirror

101 Curious Poems

By Arden Davidson

Edited and designed by Jade Maitre.
Interior illustrations by Kseniya Shagieva
Cover illustration by Helga Lebedeva

Storyberries Publishing 2019

Table of Contents

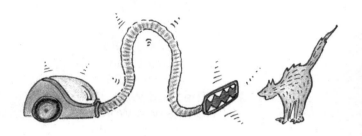

The Day I Was Born

The day I was born,
I will never forget it.
(Although they all say that I have.)
I looked around
without making a sound,
then I screamed that I wanted a bath.

But the doctors just nodded,
ignoring my pleas,
like they didn't understand what I said.
So I screamed even louder
till they gave me some powder
and tucked me away in my bed.

The day I was born,
I will always remember
as clear as a crystal sea.
For that was the day
all my fears went away
and I started the process of me.

Dirty Laundry

I hadn't washed
my socks
for 13 weeks.

My mom found out
too late
for me to warn her.

They grossed her out
so bad,
she got real mad

And made both me
and my socks
stand in the corner.

Be Careful What You Wish For

Arnie the apple hung from a tree
in an orchard a mile wide.
And every day the pickers would come
and haul dozens of apples inside.

They'd pick the prettiest of the bunch,
filling their baskets and pails.
But they always passed by Arnie,
ignoring his whines and wails.

"Please pick me!" Arnie would cry
each time the pickers sauntered by.
"I want to go inside with you!"
cried Arnie till he turned bright blue.

But the pickers ignored him day after day,
while Arnie hung there in dismay,
trying to nurse his shattered pride,
dying to be picked to be taken inside.

Each new dawn he'd do a trick
like spinning around on his twig.
But the picky pickers never stopped
for apples that weren't big

or juicy or red or bright or sweet.
Poor Arnie was none of these things.
He wasn't completely quite full grown
and he had some nicks and dings.

He dreamed what it was like inside;
lights and music all around.
Arnie just wanted to go there so badly
he flung himself to the ground.

The next day the pickers came along
and saw him lying there.
They took him inside and Arnie thought,
"This is it! I'm finally there!"

But when Arnie the Apple looked around
he realized his dreams were false,
'cause in less than 15 minutes
he was Arnie Applesauce.

Camera Shy

I'm so upset -
I'm mortified.
I need a real cool
place to hide.

I never will
let one soul see
this ugly, gross
picture of me.

I can't believe
I looked like that
for even just
one second flat.

My face looks squished.
My nose looks pug.
And my left eyeball
looks like a bug!

This photograph
must disappear.
I'd die if my friends
saw it here.

Wait...mom is talking
to my dad,
I think things might not
be so bad.

I think she's solved
my problem, yup!
She said she's gonna
blow it up!

Making Cents

I heard that thoughts
cost just a penny,
so I tried to sell mine
but I didn't have any.

I heard that some nickels
are wood, like a tree.
So I chopped up a log,
now I'm rich as can be.

I heard that girls
are a dime a dozen
So I bought me 9 sisters,
2 moms and a cousin.

I heard that a quarter
won't stretch very far.
I found out it was true
and I still have the scar.

I find money matters
to be very strange.
But I'll learn, 'cause I don't want to be
scared of change.

Ouch

I ran across the floor
and smacked into a door.
It made my nose all bloody.
And now I'm talking fuddy.

It blackened up my eye
so bad I thought I'd die.
It flattened out my face
so it looked like second base.

It knocked a couple of teeth loose.
Now I squirt when I drink orange juice.
Next time I take off runnin', I'm hopin'
the door I'm runnin' through is open.

Something In My Eye

There's something
in my eye.
If it's dust,
I think I'll cry.

If it's mud,
I think I'll scream.
If it's a fly,
I hate this dream.

If it's a spider,
it'll tickle.
If it's dead,
I'm in a pickle.

If it's a mouse,
then I'll
yell "Scram!"
But,
If it's deaf,
I'm in a jam.

If it's a fish,
I'll bawl right now.
If it's a horse,
I'll have a cow.

If it's a bee,
I'll grab its stinger.

Silly me,
it's just my finger.

Porcupine Picnics

When porcupines get
together for picnics,
Nobody has
to bring any toothpicks.

A Matter of Opinion

I can make the strangest noises
when I twist and twirl my tongue,
then stick it through my two front teeth
and whistle with my lung.

I can make the weirdest faces
when I wrinkle up my nose,
then twist my lips like pretzels
and tie my ears in bows.

I can make the coolest music
tapping turtles with a ruler.
I think I'm real creative.
My mom thinks I'm peculiar.

Asking for Trouble

I went to the pet store
and asked this guy, Steve,
"Can a cat get dog tired?"
He asked me to leave.

I went to the market
and asked this guy, Mo,
"Can an orange go plum crazy?"
He asked me to go.

I went to the circus
and asked this guy, Sam,
"Can a tiger have horse sense?"
He told me to scram.

I asked mom a question
on my way out to play.
"Can mommies give bear hugs?"
She asked me to stay.

A Timely Love Story

Noon fell in love with midnight,
but they lived twelve hours apart.
They wanted to get together so bad
to discuss matters of the heart.

But every time midnight came around,
noon was fast asleep.
And when noon was ready to get together,
midnight's sleep was deep.

They could never figure out how to meet
to hug and to kiss and to talk,
till they realized they share the very same space
on the place called the face of a clock.

Silly Footprints

I spent years
searching for a
six-footed camel.
I'd never seen it,
but I knew it existed,
'Cause I'd seen
its footprints
in the sand,
but every time
I got close,
I missed it.

I studied its
footprints in the hot,
summer sun
and everything
seemed just fine,
until I realized
four footprints were his
and two of them
were mine!

Haircut Schmaircut

Today I got a haircut
and I think I'm going to cry.
Seeing myself in the mirror this way
just makes me want to die.

The top is way too short,
and my ears stick out all funny.
The back looks like the mangled tail
of a mutant Easter bunny.

My bangs look like they lost real bad
in a game of truth or dare.
A word of advice, never ever let
your best friend cut your hair!

A Centipede Won an Award

A centipede won an award
surrounded by hundreds of fans.
Though his speech only lasted a minute,
it took hours to shake all his hands!

Games People Play

I like playing Ring Around the Rosie,
but what's a pocket full of posie?
And who the heck's this girl called Rosie?
I've asked all over town.

Maybe I'm just being nosey,
But nobody knows why pockets of posie
or circling 'round some girl named Rosie
should make us all fall down.

I also like playing Mother May I,
and though I play it every day I
still don't know what I should say, I
just don't need this noise.

Why should I say Mother May I
have some scissor steps? Today I
think I'll play a different way, I
think I'll ask for toys.

Just Checking

I have a question
for you
'cause I want to
see things clear.

If a doctor ate
an apple a day
would it make
him disappear?

Muncha Buncha Lunch

Muncha Buncha Lunch
is the nickname of a kid
Who eats everybody's lunches
that aren't locked up or hid.

If you ever turn your back on him
for even half a minute,
When you turn back to your lunch box,
that ole Muncha Bunch is in it.

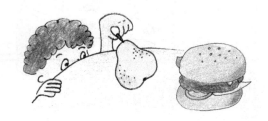

He eats chips and grapes and pears
and soup and sandwiches galore.
And when he's done with all of that,
he still can eat some more.

He munches, crunches, gulps and swallows
everything in sight.
He eats lunch for breakfast...dinner too,
and even at midnight.

I wonder what would happen
if somebody had a hunch
And sent all the school kids home at noon
except for Muncha Bunch.

Then whose bananas would he steal?
Whose pretzels would he take?
He'd probably end up eating all the chairs,
for goodness sake.

That Muncha Buncha's appetite
is just too big to stop.
Next time he tries to eat my lunch,
I'm gonna call a cop!

That will teach him not to be
so gluttonous and rude,
Cuz then all he'll have left to eat
is yucky prison food!

The Skiing Incident

It's not that I'm a wimp,
but yesterday I tried to ski,
and I've come to the conclusion now
that skiing's just not me.

I don't know why it happened
and I don't know what it meant,
But it will from now on be referred to
as "the skiing incident."

I told my dad, it's crazy,
that the logic's incomplete;
relying on those crazy shoes
to keep me on my feet.

He laughed and said, "This isn't
some deranged depravity.
Don't worry, you'll be fine, son,
just rely on gravity."

When I saw the giant mountain,
sure, it gave me quite a scare,
but that was just the onset,
it was all downhill from there.

I knew that if I didn't try,
I'd be laughed out of town,
So I rode the ski lift up
but was afraid to come back down.

I stood there for an hour
summoning my strongest will,
but just couldn't find the courage
to go zooming down that hill.

'Course I guess it didn't matter
because when I turned to go,
I slipped, and next thing I knew
I was cruising 'cross the snow.

I almost hit a tree
and then I almost hit my brother.
And of course he had to laugh
when I went flying over mother.

My face was red and frozen
and my lips were getting chapped.
I just knew I'd end up stuck in some snow bank,
forever trapped.

But that is not what happened,
I am so sorry to say.
The troubles of my ski trip
are still haunting me today.

I don't want to be a pain,
but someone better call a cop,
'cause I'm still going...
No one ever told me how to stop!

What To Do About Grandma

When grandma goes to sleep at night,
I shut all the windows and doors.
I put cotton in my ears because, well,
my grandma snores.

She snores so loud it jiggles the house
and makes the shutters shake.
One time our neighbors ran out screaming -
they thought there was an earthquake.

Another time she snored so loud
our ears and noses bled.
Now everyone runs for cover
when my grandma goes to bed.

Yes, grandma's known for snoring.
She's known all over town.
Even power saws and freight trains
tell my grandma to pipe down.

She's louder than a motor bike
or a great big thunder clap.
Oh dear! Oh no! I've got to go!
It's time for grandma's nap!

Marching to a Different Guitarist

Most people have their ups and downs
I have my side to sides.
Most people don't like mice around,
I love to give them rides.

Most people try to match their socks,
I like two different ones.
Most people want to weigh 5 lbs.
I'd rather weigh 5 tons.

For the longest time, I was afraid
that I was quite insane.
I went to many doctors
but not one could change my brain.

Then I got a diagnosis
from a genius - now I'm free.
Turns out I've got a case of
individuality!

Last Night We Had Company for Dinner

I didn't talk with my mouth full
and I sat up straight.
I kept my elbows off the table
and my fingers off my plate.

I kept my salad fork on the left
and my butter knife on the right.
And I always said "Excuse me"
to show that I'm polite.

I didn't reach across the table
or knock over any glasses.
I didn't throw my food
but I made some winning passes.

I put my napkin in my lap
to show I'm no beginner,

...but

there was so much to remember,
I forgot to eat my dinner!

Stage Fright

There's a frog in my throat,
butterflies in my stomach,
a bug in my ear
and a bee in my bonnet.

I've got ants in my pants,
so I'm begging you, Teach.
Please don't make me
give that speech.

Princess Abby and the River of Tears

In a crystal palace,
on a crystal hill,
lived a princess named Abby
and a king named Bill.

Princess Abby was not
what you'd call a great beauty.
But to find her a husband
was King Bill's duty.

He scoured the land
for a suitable suitor;
Even placed a small ad
in The Weekly Intruder.

Not a single fine prince,
nor even a bum,
came calling to marry
the princess: not one.

King Bill, how he fretted.
And the princess, she fumed.
She was sure she'd get married.
She'd always assumed

that people looked deeper
than just on the surface.
She never knew people
could be cruel on purpose.

So she went to her window
and announced to the land
that no man was worthy
of asking her hand.

For no man was willing
to swallow his pride,
to look deeper than looks;
to look deep inside.

And then Princess Abby
did a curious thing.
She stared at the sky
and she started to sing.

Her voice was so lovely,
the sky was reborn.
She sang until dusk
and she cried until morn.

PRINCE
is needed

And her tears formed a river
made purely of magic.
But the town soon found out
that the river was tragic.

It washed off their beauty
and ruined their faces,
because all their hearts
were not in the right places.

So now all the people
who'd bathed in its sin
turned as ugly outside
as they were within.

And sweet Princess Abby
was the only one left
whose beauty was envied
because of its depth.

The Spinach Problem

My friend has spinach in his teeth.
I don't know what to do.
If I tell him, he'll be mad at me.
If I don't, he'll be mad too.

If I let him walk around
with spinach hanging from his gums
how can I believe that we're true friends,
that we're true chums?

But if I'm the one who tells him,
He might think that I am mean.
My friend has spinach in his teeth,
but I don't want a scene.

Maybe if I wrote a note
and didn't sign my name.
Maybe if I gave him hints
like part of some fun game.

No, I just can't do it.
I just cannot tell my friend
that he has spinach in his teeth;
our friendship sure will end.

Uh oh, here comes Rebecca.
She is sure to make a fuss.
She'll see the spinach in his teeth
and then tease both of us.

She told him! Told him right up front!
And now he's thanking her.
I can't believe it, there they go,
great friends. Oh, I'm so sure!

So now I sit here all alone.
Shoulda spoken, I suppose.
Think I'll go tell Rebecca
she's got something in her nose.

Sticky Gum

There's gum on my shoe,
so now I can chew
while I'm walking.

There's gum in my ear,
so now I can't hear
when I'm talking.

There's gum in my eye,
so the tears that I cry
are real thick.

There's gum on my heart
so when people blow kisses,
they stick.

The Case of the Missing Cookies

I'm taking my parents to court
to prove I'm an innocent kid.
The judge will most surely agree
that they're wrong about what I did.

Just because all my fingers were sticky
and chocolate was on my face,
doesn't mean I stole those cookies.
So there! I rest my case.

What's that you say, you need more proof?
I have an alibi.
When the cookies got stolen, I was outside.
Now I ask you, why would I lie?

You have no witnesses on your side;
just circumstantial lies.
I think the real crook snuck inside
in a masterful disguise.

Maybe he was disguised as me.
I really cannot say.
All I know is I did not
steal any cookies that day.

Now judge, I ask for sympathy,
so please instruct the jury
to say that I'm not guilty
(and to say it in a hurry!)

My folks are looking quite annoyed
that I've taken things this far.
But it's not as if they caught me
with my hand in the cookie jar.

The jury's back, the verdict's in.
Guilty?! That can't be!
I gathered all the evidence
that should have set me free.

Where did I go wrong, and now
what will my sentence be?
Three years of washing dishes, no!
No way! They can't mean me!

The next time I take my parents to court
(though I doubt it will be in my youth)
I'll make sure that what I'm saying
is actually the truth.

Bye Bye Baby

Baby dolls are just for kids.
I'm way beyond them now.
Baby Lucy was my friend,
but I really don't see how.

She's just a little plastic thing
some factory worker made.
I used to let her sleep with me
but that's when I was eight.

Today I'm nine and all grown up.
Baby Lucy's in my past.
Of course, I miss her just a bit
but I'm sure that won't last.

It's time to go to bed. Alone.
My heart is filled with sorrow.
Oh, forget it all, she needs me now.
I'll be grown up tomorrow.

A Better Mousetrap

I kept a mouse
in my 'frigerator.
She guarded the food,
until mommy ate her.

Now instead of
protecting
the milk and the jelly,
she watches
the food
inside
mommy's belly.

The Land of Mites and Maybees

Long, long ago
on an island far away,
sat The Land of Mites and Maybees
to the left of Backbone Bay.

The mites were hearty creatures,
they would never hurt a soul.
But their problem was they never could
achieve a single goal.

They knew just what they wanted,
and they'd ponder it at length,
but when it came to action,
they just didn't have the strength.

The maybees were quite similar,
with only slight revisions.
They'd say "maybe this" and "maybe that",
but never reached decisions.

There was a king, King Know It All,
who loved to take advantage
of these measly mites and maybees
whom without him could not manage.

Or so they thought, for they'd been told
and learned so deep within
that there's just no sense in trying
when you know you cannot win.

And so the king, with ruling hand
grew stronger every day.
For the mites and maybees just assumed
that his was the best way.

Till one bright day, out of the blue,
a mini-mite was walking
and in his sheltered innocence,
he suddenly began talking.

"Why do we weed our gardens by hand
when it's faster with a hoe?
And why do we sled in summertime
instead of in the snow?

"Why do we paint our buildings brown,
when red is so much brighter?
And why do we carry sacks of rocks
when stones are so much lighter?"

The mini-mite kept asking more,
like a record that was broken.
Though all of them had thought these things,
none had ever spoken.

"Shhh! Pipe down!" were the frightened cries
as they worried their king would hear.
The mites and maybees looked around,
their eyes spread wide with fear.

"I'll be quiet," said the mini-mite,
"but I just have one more query.
If there's more of us than there is of him,
why is he so scary?"

The mites and maybees pondered this,
this thought that was quite new.
And as they tugged and wrestled it,
the logic in it grew.

Suddenly everything seemed so clear;
they all had minds of their own,
so why were they letting King Know It All
rule his mighty throne?

Well, it didn't take long once this thought was in place,
for weeds to be pulled out with hoes.
And it didn't take long for paint to be red
and for sleds to be used when it snows.

Soon the king got weaker, and finally left;
Left the whole kingdom far behind.
For he realized that not even he was as strong
as the power of speaking your mind.

Color Me Happy

If I were the color blue,
I'd sing sad songs for you.

If I were the color yellow,
I'd be a happy fellow.

If I were the color red
I'd look like me when I bled.

If I were the color green,
I'd grow like a big string bean.

If I were the color brown,
I'd be a chocolate town.

If I were the color pink,
I'd be a lemony drink.

If I were the color purple,
Nothing would rhyme with me.

Shoo, Shoes! Shoo!

Clickety, clackety, clackety click.
My noisy shoes just make me sick.

I can't get away with stuff since I got 'em.
(I guess that's why my mother bought 'em.)

When I try to creep to the cookie jar,
I never make it very far.

When I try to slink up and scare my cat,
I'm busted in two seconds flat.

When I try to slip in late from school
My parents know I broke their rule.

I can't play cop and look for clues.
I can't get any secret news.

I never win at hide and seek.
These shoes make me a lousy sneak!

I can't tickle my dad when he's taking a snooze.
I hate these lousy, noisy shoes!

Clackety Clickety, Clickety Clack!
(That was the sound of me taking them back).

Inside a Pen

Inside a pen
live dragons and kings,
and soldiers and wishes
and fanciful things.

Inside a pen
live mermaids and frogs
and ponies and clowns
and slop-eatin' hogs.

Inside a pen
live rainbows and dreams
and airplanes and lions
and marvelous schemes.

Inside a pen,
your hopes and your glories
are waiting for you
to write their stories.

First Things First

I often wonder what inspired
folks to try things first.
Like who was the first to blow bubbles with gum,
and what did he think when they burst?

Who was the first to count with numbers?
Who was the first to run?
Who was the first to sneeze, and goodness,
what did he think he'd done?

The first one to eat spinach
must have wondered why he did it.
The first to pick lint from his belly button
probably wouldn't admit it.

Who was the first to twist a pretzel?
Who was the first to own a cat?
Who was the first to wear underwear
and how did he feel about that?

The first to throw a frisbee
must have wondered where it went.
The first to write a letter
must have wondered where it sent.

Who was the first to use an umbrella?
Who was the first to dream?
Who was the first to have a nightmare
and who was the first to scream?

I often wonder
if they knew
they were the first, and I
often wonder
how many things
I was the first to try.

Just Doing What I'm Told

When it comes to homework,
my sister says
that studying hard is best.

My brother believes
that the best time to study
is an hour before a test.

I thought about it
and realized
I'm going to do what she says.

So I've been studying really hard
for my favorite subject...

Recess!

Fortune Teller

My name is Madam Zedora.
I can see the future clear.
I tell all my friends their fortunes.
I say what they want to hear.

I told Melissa Martin
she should marry Steven Trace.
But when she popped the question...
well, he laughed right in her face.

I read Amelia Manning's palm
and said she'd get a "B"
on her math test, but to my dismay
she got a big, fat "D."

I said to Ryan Johnson
that he'd get a brand new bike
for Christmas, but instead
he got a toy he didn't like.

My name's Madam Zedora.
I get everything all wrong.
My crystal ball says I won't be
a fortune teller long.

(Looks like I might
have got something right!)

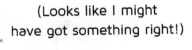

Second Hand Blues

All my clothes are second hand
just because my sister can't
button, zip or snap them anymore.

Now I'm stuck with ugly clothes
that she picked out five years ago,
and I'm afraid to walk out my front door.

Doesn't mom know I want to look cool
instead of the biggest joke in school?
Why can't I have some new clothes all my own?

These styles have never been in fashion.
C'mon mom, have some compassion.
How 'bout fronting me a little loan?

It's not my fault she got here first,
and that her taste's by far the worst.
It's not my fault and I'm not going to take it!

No more second hand for me.
I kept my promise faithfully,
but went through the entire school year naked.

The Ghost With The Most

"Boo! Boo Hoo!",
cried the ghost with the most.
"No one comes to visit me,
though I'm the perfect host.

I decorate with cobwebs,
sweep the spiders under the rug,
Yet no one ever offers me
a kind word or a hug.

I don't know what the reason is.
I don't know what could cause it,
'Cause I always, yes I always
keep my skeletons in the closet.

Sure, I may look scary
but if someone really knew me,
they wouldn't be afraid
'cause they could see
right through me."

Cone-Head

Triple decker double fudge.
Quadruple caramel topping.
When I go to the ice cream shop,
I keep the scoopers hopping.

Every flavor that exists,
and every topping too,
I make them pile on my cone
and then when they are through,

I take my ice cream cone outside
and gobble it real fast.
I have just one more thing to say...

I hope this sharp pain doesn't last.

Squirrelly Shirley

Squirrely Shirley
lived in a tree
where she hoarded her nuts
so selfishly.

No matter what happened
she wouldn't share.
Her nuts were her nuts and
she just didn't care

that Dilmont the deer
and Harry the hare
and Ronnie the robin
and Benny the bear

were hungry. As hungry
as hungry could be.
Squirrely Shirley just watched them
from high in her tree.

She laughed while she popped
each nut into her mouth,
while the others were searching for food
north and south.

Squirrely Shirley
lived in a tree
till she got so fat
she could hardly see.

Then one day she noticed
an overlooked nut
on the end of a twig
and she wanted it, but

She had gotten so heavy
the branch broke in two
and she fell to the ground;
became squirrel and nut stew.

Which just goes to show
that it's not smart to be
a selfish, fat squirrel
when you live in a tree.

Playing the Fool

My friends and I
put on a homemade play
for kids to watch.
(We invited parents too
to kinda class it up a notch.)

The play was called "The Princess"
and of course,
I was the star.
I wrote it and directed it
(that's how us big stars are!)

The audience was sitting
on the chairs
I'd made from crates,
As I stood upon the platform
that I'd built from paper plates.

The curtain lifted so I started
walking out on stage.
I said my first line perfectly -
and then I turned the page.

Everybody listened, laughed and cried...
they loved my play!
That is until my two left feet
got in my right foot's way.

I began my grand finale
(a nice tap dance with a twist)
Then I leapt into the air
but, when I came back down,
I missed.

If you can't quite get the picture,
check your local gossip page.
The caption reads "Don't Worry,
She's Just Going Through a Stage."

Looth Tooth

I've got a looth tooth
that wigglth and jigglth and wrigglth.
I move it around
but it never comth out of my mouth.
I pull it, I yank it,
I twirl it, I thpank it,
but it jutht never theems
to want to come out
of ith houth.

I'd call the Tooth Fairy,
but she'th kinda thcary,
Tho I thtill cannot theem to be free
of thith wiggly looth tooth,
that to tell you the truth,
ith makin' a thap outa me.

I'm going to give it
one thuper thtrong yank,
cuth I really could uthe thome money.
Great Scott! It's out! At last, it's out!
But now I'm talking funny.

Cow-ard

I can't. I quit.
I won't. That's it.
I'm done. I'm through.
No more.

No chance. I'm gone.
Forget it. So long.
Goodbye. I'm out
the door.

Drop it. Leave it.
Not maybe. No, never!
Not ever. No way.
No how.

You can't get me,
just three foot three
to milk that
angry cow.

Sounds Like It To Me

Tick Tock. Tick Tock.
Funny how it rhymes with clock.
Rub-a-dub, Rub-a-dub, Rub-a-dub, dub.
Funny how it rhymes with tub.

Plip, plop. Down the drain.
Funny how it rhymes with rain.
Splish, splash. Slip, slop.
Funny how it rhymes with mop.

Yummy, yummy. Slurp, slurp, slurp.
Funny how it rhymes with burp.

If words sound just like what they do,
what words, do you think, would rhyme with
you?

Baby Face

I hate my baby face.
I want a
grown up face instead.
Then I would not
be told to leave
when all
the good stuff's said.

No one would
pinch my cheeks
And Grandma Mabel,
I suppose,
would use her hanky
on herself
instead of
on my nose.

Plus, I would rule
the school
Just like
that kid
who knows karate...

The only problem left
would be
my 3 foot 9 inch body!

A Key Problem

I've practiced the piano
for just over two years
and still the sounds I make come out
aren't music to my ears.

Every key I dare to touch
sounds like a nauseous cat.
And every song I try to play
sounds even worse than that.

My Yankee Doodle Dandy
sounds a lot like Yankee Rose.
And my Chopsticks imitates the sound
of when I blow my nose.

I keep on taking lessons
in the hope that I'll improve.
But if I don't get better soon,
my family's gonna move.

I practice through the day and night
but no improvement shows.
I'm not dumb, it's just hard
to play piano with your toes!

The Vacuum Monster

I hear it start to growl
when my mom plugs in its tail.
Then its middle gets all puffed up
like the belly of a whale.

It drags my mom behind her
eating everything in sight.
It's hungry and it's angry;
prob'ly never lost a fight.

My puppy runs away from it.
My baby kitty claws it.
And we all feel so much better
when it's sleeping in the closet.

It's not that I am scared of it.
I'd never, ever be.
It's just that when it roars,
I can't hear one word on TV!

Pie in the Sky

I heard someone mention a pie in the sky
so I figured I'd eat it for fun.
"It must be delicious", I thought to myself,
"being baked in the sky by the sun."

So I got dad's old ladder out of the garage
and I grabbed me a fork and a plate.
Then I climbed to the sky, searching for that big pie -
man, my stomach and I couldn't wait!

I looked all around, but no pie to be found
and the hunger inside me was itchin'.
Then a sparrow flew by, so I said "where's the pie?"
And he answered, "Who know's? Try your kitchen!"

"That does it!" I said, "There's no pie in the sky"
I climbed sadly back to the ground.
Someone must have hoarded it all for themselves
before it could ever be found.

The big problem is, I'm still really hungry -
I guess I should learn how to bake.
I just wonder if whoever stole the pie
is the same guy who takes the cake.

The Jones's House

Don't go inside the Jones's house,
you do and you'll regret it.
Mr. Jones has a real live monster
and his wife will make you pet it.

Their kids are even stranger,
wearing snake skins in their hair.
And when it's time for dinner,
hey, you'd best get out of there.

Don't ever peek through their keyholes
or peer down their bathroom drain,
'cause a giant seahorse jumps right out
and tries to steal your brain.

Next time you're out, just be aware
where all the groans and moans is,
'cause not even the scariest haunted houses
can keep up with the Jones's.

The Mysterious Thing on My Plate

I'm not sure what my mom made me for
dinner.
I think that it's a hockey puck, no lie.
My knife won't even make a little dent.
Maybe it's a molten lava pie.

Hmmm...

I could use it as a baseball in tomorrow's game.
I could toss it in the river with the other rocks.
I could take it into school for Tuesday's show
and tell.
I could kick it down the street for twenty
blocks.

This hard and crusty thing that's on my plate
has put me in a rather foul mood,
because it could be a million different things,
but the one thing it could never be is food.

Talking in Circles

Annabelle Merkles only talks in circles.
She won't talk any other way.
So when Annabelle Merkles gets inside of circles,
It's best to stay out of her way.

She'll talk going 'round a carousel.
She'll chat in a hula hoop.
But ask her to play four square
and you've knocked her for a loop.

During ring around the rosey,
her talking is absurd.
But take her to a square dance
and she won't utter a word.

She'll surround herself with fruit loops
or a big old onion ring,
but mention a square meal
and Annabelle won't say a thing.

She'll gossip while tying a lasso,
or even while forming a noose,
but ask her to tie a square knot
and it's really just no use.

Because Annabelle Merkles only talks in circles.
She refuses to speak at an angle.
But I'm quite sure she'd shout,

"Please let me out!"

from inside the Bermuda Triangle.

Truth or Dare

I dare you to walk up
to Heather McGee
and hand her a great big
bumble bee.

I dare you to go
to Marissa's place
and shove a cream pie
right into her face.

I dare you to jump out
at Donald Deluth
and try to knock out
his great big front tooth.

I dared Pauly Peplock
all of these things
and he did each one,
but he got the bee stings

and he got the cream face
and he lost a tooth.
Now he's not big on dares,
to tell you the truth.

Critical Condition

A bee without its stinger
is like a porcupine without quills
is like an ant without its feelers
is like a fish without its gills
is like a goose without its feathers
is like a kangaroo with no pouch
is like a turtle without its shell
is like a dad without its couch.

Bubble Trip

I blew a bubble
and hopped inside
so that beautiful bubble
could give me a ride.

I floated past treetops
and airplanes and stars.
I soared over buildings
and sidewalks and cars.

I thought it was great
till mom said I'm in trouble.
Boy, she really knows how
to burst a guy's bubble!

Getting Unbored

Bored, bored, bored.
There's nothing good to do.
I don't feel like playing football.
I don't want to paint things blue.

I'm not in the mood for TV,
and I'm sick of hide and seek.
Bored, bored, bored, bored, bored, bored, bored.
I've been bored for a week.

I no longer like my train set,
and my bike is getting old.
All my friends are outside playing,
but I think it's much too cold.

I don't feel like doing anything,
but doing nothing's just as bad.
Bored, bored, bored, bored, bored, bored, bored.
This boredom makes me mad.

I'm tired of my race cars,
and my games are all the pits.
I no longer like my checkers
and I hate my baseball mitts.

I just sit here on the sofa
listening closely to each breath.

If I don't do something soon
I'll probably bore myself to death.

Uh oh. Here comes my mother,
with some chores for 'you know who'.
"I can't clean my room now, Mom!
I've got way too much to do!"

Rich Kid

I found a quarter on the sidewalk.
Boy, am I excited!
I'm feeling mighty, mighty rich
and I don't plan to hide it.

I think I'll buy a baseball.
Hmmmm. I don't have quite enough.
Instead I'll buy a rag doll.
Boy, this shopping stuff is tough.

Okay, I'll buy a pizza.
No, I'm still a little shy.
How 'bout a bag of onion rings?
Well, it was worth a try.

I've searched for half the day now
for one thing I can afford,
and now I have to tell you
that I'm growing rather bored.

I guess I'll buy some gumballs
so that I can finally end it.
It's amazing how long a quarter lasts
when you can't afford to spend it.

Sent To My Room

I broke a dish
and mom got mad.
She sent me to my room
because she said that I was bad.

So I'm sitting here
on my comfy bed
with my big screen TV
right in front of my head

and my favorite toys
spread around me like friends
and my video game
that never ends,

And I'm wondering what
my mother meant
when she said my room
was a punishment.

Achoo!

Sneezing is normal.
(I suppose.)
But one time while sneezing,
Cheryl Lynn Rose
shot a small dragon
out of her nose.
This wasn't normal.
(Goodness knows).
And it really surprised
poor Cheryl Lynn Rose,
and the dragon too
(I suppose).
'Cause nobody knew
that he lived in her nose.

Well, the dragon quite liked
sweet Cheryl Lynn Rose,
and lately he follows
wherever she goes.
I heard that he's planning
to someday propose
to sweet little Cheryl Lynn,
Cheryl Lynn Rose.

But she feels
quite different.
(Goodness knows).

She never does
want him
to propose.
He thinks they're friends.
She knows they're foes;
How'd a dragon like that
come from such a cute nose?

Now every time Cheryl Lynn
huffs and blows,
she grabs her nostrils;
makes them close.
She's afraid someone else
has taken a doze
inside her sneezing
little nose.

Poor little, poor little
Cheryl Lynn Rose.
So many troubles.
So many woes.
She's stuck with a dragon
she never chose,
all 'cause she sneezed him
out of her nose.
He'll always be with her
(I suppose.)

There they goes.

The Hard Way

I've got a rabbit's foot
and a four leaf clover.
A lucky penny
and a troll named Dover.

I've crossed my fingers,
I've wished on stars.
And for extra
safe measures,
I've wished on Mars.

I've avoided all ladders
and black cats as well.
Even went to a witch
for a fifty cent spell.

Now I'm armed
and I'm ready
to do my best.
Next time I'll just study
for my history test.

I Won't Say A Word

There are words I'm not allowed to say.
I really don't know why.
But once when I said one of them,
I made my mother cry.

I'm still not quite sure what it meant.
(It slipped out unexpected).
But my mother told my father,
and for now, I'm not respected.

My father told my neighbor
and my neighbor told his kid.
Now I'm an outcast at my school
and I don't know what I did!

The school told everyone in town,
that bad word that I said.
Now my preacher told my father
that I need help in the head.

I'll never use that word again.
I'll lament and I'll repent.
I only wish I had a clue
what the heck that darn word meant!

Animal Talk

I think that I've got it all figured out...
what animal talk is all about.

"Moo" means excuse me, that's my
milk you're takin'.
"Oink" means quit lookin' at me
like I'm bacon.

"Nay" means no shoes, no shirt,
no ride.
"Baa" means, gee lately it's
colder outside.

"Arf" means my tail
is my very best feature.
"Meow" means I'm such
an exquisite creature.

"Quack" means this water
is turning quite icy.
"Hiss" means you look
so delicious and spicy.

"Roarrr" means I am
the king of the beasts.
"Honk" means I am
the queen of the geese.

"Grrrr" means I'll eat you
when you go for a walk.
Boy am I glad
I speak animal talk!

Bad Timing

My watch is broken
so I can't tell the time.
I don't know if it's midnight
or quarter past nine.

I don't know if I'm eating
my dinner or lunch.
I don't know if I should be
in bed or at brunch.

I've broken my watch
and I haven't a clue
what in the world
I'm supposed to do.

What time could it be?
I hope that it's three
because that's when my favorite cartoon's
on TV.

I think I hear school bells
and if that's the case,
I'm in the right time
but I'm in the wrong place!

When You're First, You Don't Know Any Better

If the chicken came before the egg,
the first hen to lay one must have vowed
never again to lift her leg,
cuz when she did, her insides fell out.

But if the egg came before the chicken,
the chicken inside must've, under his breath,
sworn if he kept up his fussin' and kickin',
he'd scramble himself to death.

Flying Popcorn

A piece of popcorn
escaped from the pan
and flew across the kitchen
like Superman.

It ping-ponged back and forth
between the oven and the freezer.
Then it shot up to the ceiling
like a daredevil trapeezer.

I tried and tried to catch it,
but it never missed a trick.
So finally I gave up
and ate a liquorice stick.

A Secret Service

I've got a secret
that no one else can know.
I've got a secret
and I'll never let it go.

You can torture me with spiders;
Pull my hair until it rips,
But I promised that this secret
would never leave my lips.

You can tickle me with feathers.
You can tell me I'm a creep.
But this secret is a secret
that I've vowed to always keep.

You can swing me till I'm dizzy.
You can lock me in a cell.
You can throw me in a pig sty
and I still won't ever tell,

'Cause I promised that this secret
will forever be unspoken
and the secret to a promise is,
it can't be broken.

Bad Habit Marvin

Do you know Bad Habit Marvin?

He bites his nails
and grabs dog's tails,
and stubs his toes
and picks his nose,

And burps out loud
(it makes him proud)
to grind his teeth
and smell his feet

And shake his head
and wet his bed.

He tickles girls
and yanks their curls
and steals their books
with dirty looks.

He never washes
or wears galoshes,
or helps mom cook
or reads a book.

Bad Habit Marvin,
you know him well,
And every time he's near,
you yell,

"Bad Habit Marvin,
why ya act so dumb?!"
But he can't answer back
'cause he's sucking his thumb.

Under the Weather

Lizzy the Lizzard
got caught in a blizzard
and she didn't know what to do.

So she yelled at the sky
"Will you please tell me why
you make all of this snow like you do?"

Feeling under attack,
The sky answered back,
"It's none of your business, Sweet Pea."

That made Lizzy mad,
so she tried to act bad
shouting, "you don't begin to scare me!"

Well that wasn't true,
which the sky surely knew
so he upsized the snow flakes to hail.

Then he added some lightning
to make it more frightening
and Lizzy soon started to wail.

"That was truly unkind,
now I never will find
my way home - you're a mean, vicious sky!"

"I was just having fun"
said the sky, "but I'm done.
Just whatever you do, please don't cry."

He then hung out the sun,
melting snow by the ton,
so that Lizzie could see her way clear.

"That was nice of you sky",
Lizzie said, "Well good-bye,
You've dried up my very last tear."

So Lizzie the Lizzard
survived the bad blizzard
but the sun turned her skin into leather.

Now she's begging for snow,
which just goes to show,
that you don't want to mess with the weather!

One More Chance

Oh no! I've lost my chance!
I just can't find it anywhere.
It was in my back pants pocket
But now, darn it - it's not there.

Just yesterday, I had my chance.
Now suddenly it's gone.
And the worst part is that was the one chance
I depended on.

I only had one chance.
but still I let it slip away.
I'd give anything if I could have
my one chance back today.

It was truly the chance of a lifetime.
but it fell out of my pants.
I wonder where you go
to get a second chance?

Freckle Bath

I'll tell you what I tried to do,
if you promise you won't laugh.
I tried to wash my freckles off
while I was in my bath.

I scrubbed and rubbed and rubbed and scrubbed
with my washcloth, soap and water.
I tried it with the water cold.
I tried with it much hotter.

But my freckles wouldn't budge an inch,
although I tried my best.
So I kept the freckles where they were
and washed away the rest.

Honk Goes the Moose

If a moose
turned into a goose,
he'd have
tail feathers
for a caboose.

His mouth
would become a beak.
So he'd honk
when he tried to speak.

His feet
would turn
orangish red.
His antlers
would fall
from his head.

I really feel sorry
for mooses
who somehow
get turned
into gooses.

They Say

They say little girls
are sugar and spice.
They say that lightning
never strikes twice.

They say that you're only
as old as you feel.
They say we should not
reinvent the wheel.

They say you should save
for a rainy day.
But what I want to know is,

Who are THEY?

The Animal Diet

Part I. Bones

If I had a tail,
I'd wag it all day.
If I had claws,
I'd dig a bay.

If I had a bone,
I'd always play.
But if I had to eat dog food,
I'd run away.

Part II. Worms

If I had a beak,
I'd quack to talk.
If I had wings
I'd forget how to walk.

If I thought I could fly, then
I'd give it a whirl
but if I had to eat earthworms,
I'd probably hurl!

Part III. Grass

If I had hooves
I'd stomp the ground.
If I could moo
I'd love my sound.
If I gave milk
I'd want a cup,
But if I had to eat grass
I'd throw it up!

Part IV. Summary

I hope I haven't grossed you out,
but that's how animals eat.
Horses eat oats, mice eat stale cheese
and rats eat spoiled meat.

Spiders eat flies and flies eat skin,
and cats lick their own fur...

If I were not a human kid,
I'd starve to death for sure!

What Did People Do?

What did people do before they had TVs?
Or video games, or DVDs?
Or streaming music or crazy apps?
Or roller blades or Google Maps?

What did they do?
How did they have fun?

Of course, in the year 3001...

Some kid will look back
and start wondering about
how we lived without things
that he can't live without.

Play on Words

Words are fun to play on.
Especially one's with A's,
Because you can slide right down 'em
and then land on top of j's.

You just line them in a row
or stack them like a big skyscraper.
It's like a word game,
only you don't need a piece of paper!

The j's and q's and y's and g's
are fun to swing upon.
Their hooks are very comfortable
and their stems are nice and long.

You can climb t's like a fire pole.
You can do the same with i's.
The b's have built in cubby holes
and o's are the perfect size

for rolling down a grassy hill
while you're curled up in their centers.
And those who created w's
were masterful inventors,

Because w's make great seesaws;
nothing else can rock you higher. ·
Plus, when you turn them upside down;
You rule an "m"-pire.

Words are fun to play on;
for good times, you just can't beat 'em.
Plus, once you're all grown up,
I've heard you even get to eat 'em!

Naming Things

I love to give things names.
I think I'll call you Hal.
I'll also call your sweater Fred
and your umbrella, Big Al.

I can't stop naming things.
I name everything I see.
My baseball's name is Sherman
and my bat's named Woe S. Me.

My shoes are Brett and Bart.
My socks are Rick and Rack.
My jeans are Walkin' Willie
and my T-shirt's named Bo Jack.

My eyes are Moose and Juice.
My feet are Stan and Fran.
I name everything I see
and I name everything I can.

When my sis says pass the salt,
I say, "Don't you mean Michelle?"
When my brother wants my jacket,
I say, "Don't you mean Miguel?"

Finally, the other day,
my mother sat me down.
She said, "You must stop naming
everything you see in town."

I promised I would stop it.
Then I named her necklace Bud.
So now I have a new name of my own....

MUD!

Hard to Swallow

When I tell people that
I stole an alligator's guts,
They usually look at me and
tell me something like "you're nuts!"

When I tell people I
played football with the Green Bay Packers,
They usually look at me and
say, "I'm sorry, but you're crackers!"

When I tell people I own
half of Florida's cabanas,
They usually look at me
and say, "my friend, you are bananas!"

And when I tell people
that I clean my bedroom with a rake,
They usually look at me
and say "you're truly a fruit cake"

I like to tell strange stories,
And they're all made up, of course.
But being told I'm crazy
makes me hungry as a horse!

(I still haven't figured out why... guess
I'm a few sandwiches shy...)

Shaking Hands

Why is it that people always shake hands
when they meet upon the street?
Why isn't shaking their noses or ears
the proper way to greet?

Why do people shake and nod
their heads for yes and no?
Why not wiggle their belly buttons,
or tickle their own toe?

Why do people raise their hands
when they want to give an answer?
Why not shout or spit or pout
or spin 'round like a dancer?

Where did people learn these rituals?
In Iceland or Hong Kong?
Who was the first to try them out,
and how did they catch on?

Well, it's time for me to go,
so it's time to wave goodbye.
My hand is wobbling in the air,
but I'm still not quite sure why.

Bundled Up

I've got my turtleneck and sweater
and my thickest socks and pants,
my jacket and my hat and scarf
and mittens for my hands.

Button. Zipper. Snap.
I'm snugly fastened in.
But I think I'll need a day or two
to get back out again.

Sprouts and Beans

I hate brussel sprouts! I hate lima beans!
My mom says they're great. I don't know what she means.
'Cause I hate them! I hate them! I'd rather eat sand
or fire or gravel or a big rubber band.

I sit at the table refusing to swallow.
I don't care that my stomach feels empty and hollow.
I won't let those vegetables slide down my throat.
I'm no garbage disposal! I'm no billy goat!

I spread them out on my plate so it seems
that I've eaten some sprouts and I've tasted some beans.
But mom's much too smart to fall for my tricks.
I'll be sitting at this table till I turn 96!

She won't let me eat cake, or just leave the table
till I've cleaned my plate, but I swear I'm not able.
I don't want to make trouble or cause any scenes
but I hate brussel sprouts and I hate lima beans!

Where can I hide them? Oh what can I do?
Come over here Sparky, I'll give some to you.
No, he won't eat this, he's too picky for that.
(He looks like a dog, but he acts like a cat.)

I could hide them in the flowers,
or stash them in my napkin.
I could do some pocket stuffin'
or some really good cheek packin'.
I could slip them in my underwear,
but that would feel too funny.
I'd give anything to leave this table -
even all my money!

My mom is getting mad
because my family's done with dinner.
They're watching Wheel of Fortune
and I want to see the winner.
But I'll be stuck here at this table
for the next three Halloweens.
I hate brussel sprouts and I hate lima beans!

Band-Aid Mania

I love to wear band-aids.
They make me look cool.
I show them off
when I go to school.

I put them on cuts
and scratches and bruises.
My beautiful band-aids
have so many uses.

I put them on scars
and on patches of skin
where a scrape or a nick
never even has been.

They're all over my arms,
legs, knees, elbows and hips.
I'd tell you more about them
but I've got one on my lips.

The Adventures of Petty Popperkosh

Little Petty Popperkosh
went out for an evening stroll.
Then suddenly she came across
a mean and ugly troll.

He asked her what her name was,
then he said it beared repeating,
'cause a troll with his good taste
likes to know who he is eating.

"Petty Popperkosh, what a pretty name",
he said as if to win her.
"Now that we've been introduced,
come here and be my dinner."

"You can't eat me yet!", sweet Petty warned,
"You haven't had your salad.
Here, eat some grass and some nice, green leaves.
Then your dinner will be valid."

So the troll ate the greens and he licked his lips,
quite ready for the main course.
But before he could approach,
Petty shouted with reproach,
"Wait! You have to eat your soup first, of course."

So she poured rainwater in a tulip bulb
and the horrid troll sucked it away.
"Now I'm ready!", he said with a smile.
"I've got no time for one more delay."

"But you can't eat me yet! You can't eat me yet!",
Petty pleaded with tears on her face.
"What now?!", growled the troll with an evil frown.
"Well, first you must say grace."

So the angry troll sighed and closed his eyes
and began to thank God for his food.
Till Petty stuffed lizards in his open mouth
and the troll cried out, "Hey! That was rude!"

But he chewed and he swallowed the lizards right down,
Then he fell on his side with a moan,
Wailing "I'm too full to eat you now!"
Petty Popperkosh, go home!

Too Many Hats

I've got too many hats
for just one little head.
Got a ski hat for winter,
and a night cap for bed.

Got a felt hat, a silk hat;
two or three corduroy.
Even got one for when
I feel like a cowboy.

I wear my beret
to pretend I'm in France.
And my sombrero's great
for a Mexican dance.

When I wear my top hat,
I feel like a magician.
My straw hat implies
I'm a country musician.

I've got too many hats,
everyone thinks I'm crazy.
Including my dad
and my big sister, Daisy.

They said my hats make me
act like a twit.
So I went to a shrink,
and now none of them fit.

Video Star

I'd hate to star in my own video game,
Chased by monsters and bullets and warriors;
Forever avoiding eternal androiding
While battling evil destroyers.

No, I wouldn't like being in a video game
No matter what dangers I'm braving
Because what if right when I reach the next level,
Someone shuts off the game without saving?!

It's Raining Gumballs

It's raining gumballs!
It's raining gumballs!
It's quite a wondrous treat.
They're falling from
the clouds above
and bouncing off the street.

It's raining gumballs!
It's raining gumballs!
A sticky, spectacular shower.
I try to catch them
in my mouth
for hour upon hour.

It's raining gumballs!
It's raining gumballs!
I'm not sure of the reason,
But I'm glad instead of
just the four,
we've not got gumball season!

The Island of Lost Socks

If you look down in your washing machine
you'll probably see a trap door.
It's actually always been there.
You just never saw it before.

It's easy to find your way through.
You just open it with three knocks.
And behind it you'll find a river that leads
to the Island of Lost Socks.

The natives of this island
are the socks that got away
from the awful, terrible life
of smelling feet all day.

Now they run around in the sunshine
enjoying magnificent views,
and knowing they'll never again
have to fill anybody's shoes.

They never get holes, runs or snags.
They never get sold at half price.
They always are warm and fresh smelling,
'Cause this is sock paradise.

So the next time you notice a few of your socks
have vanished without a trace,
don't bother to look in the laundry,
'cause they're in a much happier place.

The Belly Button Brag

My favorite part of my body
is my belly button, yes.
My belly button's very cool.
Know why? You'll never guess.

It's not an inny or an outy.
It's kind of in between.
And when I wear a bathing suit,
it's so proud to be seen.

People love my belly button.
(It's not just in my head).
It's what I'll be remembered for
far long after I'm dead.

My tombstone will display the words:
Here lies Mitchell McGee.
The only guy who ever had
a belly button on his knee.

The Bean Scene

I love beans.
They're a wonderful treat.
Beans are my favorite
thing to eat.

Not string beans
or green beans
or baked beans,
that's silly.

The beans I like best
are the ones made of jelly!

Wind or Sun?

If I had to choose,
If I had to pick one,
I'd give up the wind
'fore I'd give up the sun.

'Cause without the wind
you can't fly a kite,
but without the sun,
it's always night.

(And that means it's always bedtime).

Funny Face

If I could choose
a different face,
I'd start with lips
all made of lace.

I'd trade my eyes
for two blue marbles
and make my eyebrows
two big barbells.

I'd choose my ears
from ribbons and bows.
Then all I'd have left to pick
is my nose.

Compliments

Janie Debeers
says I have big ears.
Sally McPlatt
says I'm too fat.
Ronnie Segall
says I'm too tall.
Jenny Ann Wong
says my hair's too long.

Know what I say
when they say things like that?

Jesus' hair was longer
than mine.
Abraham Lincoln was
rather tall.
Santa Claus is jolly
and fat,
and I'm proud
that I look like them all.

Wondering About Spaghetti

I've always wondered
why spaghetti
comes in such long strands.
It's hard to keep it on your fork,
or even in your hands.

I've always wondered
why spaghetti
is served on a dinner plate.
Why not eat it in a sandwich
or a thick spaghetti shake?

I've always wondered
why spaghetti
is spelled such a funny way.
Why don't they take the 'h' out,
or maybe move the 'a'?

I've always wondered
why spaghetti
has tomato sauce plopped on top.
Why not grape jelly or chocolate cream,
or for that matter, red soda pop.

I've always wondered
why spaghetti
is my number one entree.
Must be because spaghetti
is just so much fun to say.

Decisions Decisions

If innocence cost
fifty cents and
crime cost just a dime,
I'd reach into my
pocket for two quarters
every time.

If joy was way on
down the road
and thrills came by
real fast,
I'd put on my good
hiking shoes
and make my
journey last.

If a good friend had
a sprinkler
and a bad friend
had a pool,
I'd be jumping
through that sprinkler,
every day,
right after school.

Wanna know how I
can choose right

when decisions
come along?
Because if my gut
feels funny,
then I know
I'm choosing wrong.

Sweet Dreams

If I could build my dream house,
I'd make the bricks from cherries.
I'd build the walls with waffles
and the roof with chocolate berries.

I'd have candy canes for trees
and green icing for the grass;
Plus a driveway made of sugar
and a pond of sassafras.

If I could build my dream house,
I would probably never pout
because then I'd know what Home Sweet Home
is really all about.

Rubber Boy

Bouncy. Bouncy. Bouncy.
I'm the boy who's made of rubber.
I bounce all over school, and then
I bounce all over mother.

From floor to ceiling,
wall to wall,
I bounce down every
empty hall.

I bounce on sidewalks.
Bounce on seas.
Bounce. Bounce. Bounce
up to the trees.

I bounce atop
my sister's head.
I bounce atop
my brother's bed.

I bounce from state to state.
I bounce from town to town.
I bounce from star to star
and then I bounce back to the ground.

I'm the boy who's made of rubber.
I bounce from sky to dirt.
And it would be the perfect life,
If only it didn't hurt!

Nonsense Day

I'm declaring today
Nonsense Day.
Nothing can make any sense.
And to show you its full glory
let me tell a little story
that signifies my own experience.

A blind man wanted to see a movie
so he called on a few of his friends.
"Sounds good" said the deaf man
as his dog meowed
and his boy cow jumped under the fence.

I felt the warm snow
melt the toe on my hand
as I backstroked across the ceiling.
Then later that night
when the sun came up bright,
I jumped to my feet while still kneeling.

I saw a bald man
brushing his hair
while he sunbathed beneath the moon.
Then a fly with no wings
and a bee with no stings
threw a New Year's Eve party in June.

A mouse with small ears
who thought cheese was disgusting,
stuffed his tail in the shirt of his pants.
Then a cat with a bone
drove a big telephone
all the way to London, France.

If you like this story,
then make up your own.
Nonsense is so easy, it's true.
But if you think you can't make it,
you don't have to fake it,
just talk like your parents do.

Bad Shot Betty and the Shooting Gallery

Bad Shot Betty went
to the fair,
hoping to win
a teddy bear.
She laid down her dollar
and promptly took aim
at the ducks in the new
shooting gallery game.

Her first shot
went flying clear up
through the ceiling.
Her second shot
sent the poor barkers
a-reeling.
Her third hit a plane
as it flew overhead.
Her fourth
whacked a bumble bee,
killing it dead.

"Just one shot left",
Betty said to herself
as she gazed at the
teddy bear
up on the shelf.

"Gotta hit me a duck.
Gotta do it today."
Betty lifted her gun
as the crowd
moved away.

Well, she pulled back
that trigger
and the pellet
then flew to the top
of the booth,
and then
off the sides, too.

It bounced all around
like a wild
jumping bean-
the craziest shot
anyone ever seen!

Then lo and behold,
it bounced off the floor,
then bounced
off the table,
then bounced
a bit more,
till it bounced
one more time
and of all
the dumb luck,

that pellet
bounced right
off a big yellow duck.

"I won it! I won it!",
Betty shouted with glee,
feeling as happy
as happy
could be.

Betty took home
her teddy,
still bursting with pride,
so relieved she had won
before anyone died.

Mr. Fireworks

How tall is his ladder?
It must be quite high
to paint all those stars
on the 4th of July.

Something to Remember

The other day at recess,
I fell flat on my face.
The other children gathered 'round
to laugh at my disgrace.

The other day in homeroom,
I fell out of my chair.
The other children gathered 'round
to laugh at my despair.

The other day, in math class,
I sat atop a pin.
The other children gathered 'round
to laugh at my chagrin.

I could have cried. Instead, I laughed
with dignity and rhythm.
Because no one can be laughing at you
when you're laughing with 'em.

Parts is Parts

Corn has ears
but cannot hear.
Spuds have eyes
but cannot see.
Cups have lips
but cannot kiss.
Chairs have legs
but can't run free.

Combs have teeth
but cannot bite.
Bread has heels
but cannot walk.
Clocks have hands
but cannot clap.
Streams have mouths
but cannot talk.

I wonder why
some things
have names
that people's parts
have too,
when their parts can't
do any
of the things
that ours can do.

The Great Homework Land Caper

There's a place on the other
side of the sun
called Homework Land, and
it's not much fun.
Everyone studies from
morning till night.
There's no time to go skating
or go fly a kite.

There's no time for watching
cartoons on TV.
There's no time for building a
house in a tree.
There's not even time to eat
any ice cream.
And the worst part of all is
there's no time to dream.

Arithmetic, Science and
Grammar and Spelling,
History, Reading, there's
really no telling
if the homework will ever
come to an end.
I feel sorry for kids in
Homework Land.

I've decided that I should
help them escape.
I'll chart out a plan, then I'll
make it take shape.
I'll burn all their papers and
pencils and books;
I'll stash tests in weird places
where nobody looks.

I'll drain out the ink from
each one of their pens.
And I'll throw all their
teachers in lion-filled dens.
I'll chop all their desks up
into firewood,
and erase all the words on
their blackboards for good.

Then I'll rescue the children
who never have fun
from the world on the other
side of the sun.
And Homework Land will no
longer exist.
Then The Village of Chores
will be next on my list.

What's Weird About a Mirror

What's weird about a mirror
is that I can never see
what my mirror looks like
without me.

I've peeked at it 'round corners
but my forehead I still see.
It still sees me.

I've hung down from the ceiling
by my ankles and my toes,
but it still knows.

I've tried to run right past it,
but as fast as I can go,
I still show.

What's weird about a mirror is
that I have never known
what my mirror looks like
all alone.

Forever, Child

I give you permission
to act your shoe size,
'cause who wants to act their age?
And I think it's quite alright
to ask for a night light
when the bed monsters are let out of their cage.

I see nothing at all wrong
with belting out a song
in the middle of a long and boring Monday.
And I offer no good reason
why the cold and snowy season
should mean you can't enjoy an ice cream sundae.

I've no problem whatsoever
with playing in bad weather
or even making pancakes in the mud.
And I feel it's quite okay
to save for a rainy day
as long as you aren't waiting for a flood.

Growing up's exciting
and it probably seems inviting,
but growing up too fast is not too clever.
You'll know it in your gut
when you're really ready, but
if you're lucky you'll feel like a kid forever.

About the Author

Arden has been writing poetry practically since she was old enough to hold a pencil.

She was born in Texas but has resided in Ohio most of her life.

Arden currently runs her own freelance writing business, yet she has continued to write for fun as well - and fun is the key word when it comes to her hilarious and highly praised children's poems.

Her poems are funny, and at the same time, charmingly insightful. Kids, teachers and parents have all fallen in love with Arden's refreshing look at being a child, through the eyes of one who never completely grew up.

Storyberries Publishing

Read and listen to our free books at
Storyberries.com !